CW00384572

singing time!

grade 4

Step by step instructions for
ABRSM and other singing exams

David Turnbull

BOSWORTH   8-9 Frith Street, London, W1D 3JB

Other series by David Turnbull include:

Singing Time!
Grades 1, 2 and 3, uniform with this volume.

Aural Time!
Practice for ABRSM and other examinations. Separate teachers' books for Grades 1–8. Pupils' books available for Grades 4 with 5, 6, 7 and 8. CDs for Grades 6, 7 and 8.

Theory Time!
Step-by-step instruction for ABRSM Theory and other examinations. Grades 1–5.

Scale Time!
Step-by-step instruction for ABRSM Piano scales, arpeggios and broken chords. Grades 1–6. Separate books for each grade.

Music Processing and text setting by Note-orious Productions Ltd.
Cover Design by Miranda Harvey
Project Editor - Heather Ramage
Printed in United Kingdom by Printwise (Haverhill) Limited, Suffolk.

Bosworth
8–9 Frith Street, London W1D 3JB
Exclusive distributors:
Music Sales Ltd., Newmarket Road, Bury St Edmunds, Suffolk IP33 3YB

Singing Time! Grade 4

Introduction

This book follows the pattern of *Singing Time!* Grades 1-3. Songs are combined with instruction about keys and other rudiments.

You can learn a lot about singing from books like this, but you will learn much more if you also have a good teacher, and listen to experienced singers.

Some of the songs in this book were composed to words in foreign languages. English translations are always printed and are fully acceptable in examinations, but you are strongly advised to sing in the original language. Translations are only a second-best option, as English vowels and consonants often have no exact equivalent in other tongues. To help you, listen to a good speaker of the language in question, and to recordings.

This book contains enough material for Grade 4 ABRSM Singing (2004 syllabus). For this examination, **one** song must be chosen from **each** of the current lists A, B and C. In addition, an unaccompanied traditional song must be offered of the candidate's own choice, with a performance time of between one and two minutes. Candidates must give the examiner a list of songs at the beginning of the examination. All songs must be sung **from memory**.

List A songs in this book are: *Salley In Our Alley; Blow, Blow, Thou Winter Wind!; Since First I Saw Your Face; Man Is For The Woman Made* and *O Cessate Di Piagarmi*. **List B** songs are *Sandmännchen; Die Zufriedenheit; Abendlied; An Die Laute; Die Waise* and *O Mistress Mine*. **List C** songs are *One Hand, One Heart* and *Consider Yourself*.

All the other songs are traditional, any one of which may be sung unaccompanied in the traditional section. Chord indications are included here to help **in practice only**.

Many singers find sight-singing difficult, so this skill is stressed throughout, and the songs in this book are grouped by key.

Before making your final choice of examination songs, sing through as many songs in the book as possible in the printed keys. You can always choose to sing the song in a different key later if necessary. In examinations, songs may be transposed to any key to suit the voice of the performer, and **any** printed edition of the songs is acceptable.

On page 48 there is a list of foreign terms used in music. More help with theory can be found in my *Theory Time!* series, and with aural tests in my *Aural Time!* Grade 4. All these books are published by Bosworth/Music Sales.

Some pupils worry about singing from memory. However, this is essential if you are to sing expressively, and isn't very difficult. You will soon improve with practice and find that after only one or two attempts with the music, you know more of the words by heart than you think!

Thanks are due to my wife for translations and help, to the project editor Heather Ramage, and to the engravers at Note-orious Productions Ltd.

David Turnbull

Part 1

Warming Up

Start every practice with some of these exercises.

1 Breath control

Breathe at the end of every bar. Sing to six, then eight, then ten.

2 Vowel Practice

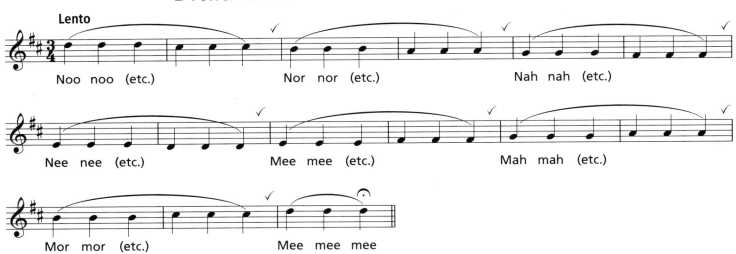

3 Control of dynamics

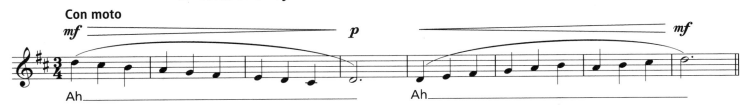

4 Arpeggios, to extend range

5 Improving resonance

Start each note by humming on 'Mm', and then follow with vowels in turn.

6 Diction

Sing slowly at first, then faster. Use lips, teeth and tongue for clear consonants.

Words by Gilbert, music by Sullivan

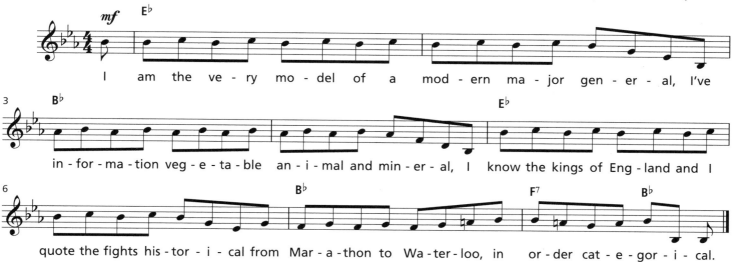

I am the ve - ry mo - del of a mod - ern ma - jor gen - er - al, I've in - for - ma - tion veg - e - ta - ble an - i - mal and min - er - al, I know the kings of Eng - land and I quote the fights his - tor - i - cal from Mar - a - thon to Wa - ter - loo, in or - der cat - e - gor - i - cal.

Learning New Songs

- Read over, aloud, the **words** of the song.
- Clap the **rhythm** of the words, counting as you clap. Do this slowly at first.
- Find the **key** of the song.
- Look at the **intervals** between the notes.
- Decide where to **breathe**. As far as possible, take breaths at punctuation marks, or during rests.
- Make sure that you understand and observe all **directions** about dynamics, etc.
- Remember that songs new to you make excellent sight-singing practice.

Learn To Stand Still!

Many singers disturb themselves, and listeners, by involuntary movements of the body, including the eyes. Practise the ability to sing from a still position. Some songs, especially songs from operas and shows, can involve considered movements, but these must always be carefully practised with the guidance of your teacher. Stand up straight, but don't become stiff. Make sure that your position allows you to breathe freely and correctly.

Memorising Intervals

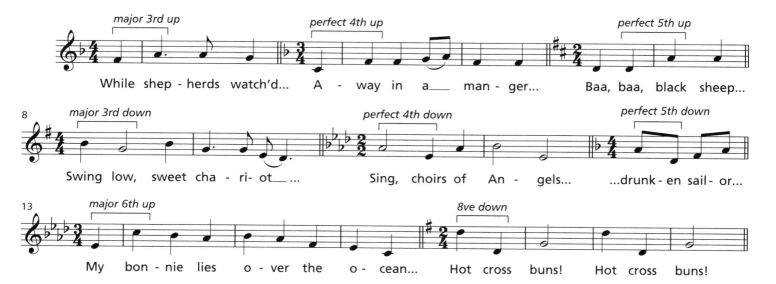

While shep - herds watch'd... A - way in a___ man - ger... Baa, baa, black sheep...

Swing low, sweet cha - ri - ot___ ... Sing, choirs of An - gels... ...drunk - en sail - or...

My bon - nie lies o - ver the o - cean... Hot cross buns! Hot cross buns!

Part 2

Songs in C and G Majors

Before starting a song, sing the arpeggio of its key. Sing the notes in one of these ways:

- Sing to letter names:

C E G C' G E C

- *or* sing to numbers (When written, Roman numerals are preferable):

I III V I' V III I

- *or* sing to 'sol-fa' names. Notes of major scales are named (in ascending order) *doh, ray, me, fah, soh, la, te* and top *doh*:

doh me soh doh' soh me doh

Botany Bay starts on the *fifth* note of the scale of C major. It needs a strong, rhythmic approach.

I II III IV V VI VII I'

Botany Bay

English Traditional

The melody of *An Die Laute* starts on G, the fifth note of the scale of C major.

An Die Laute
(To The Lute)

Franz Schubert D.905
Words by J.F. Rochlitz
translated by E.D. Turnbull

send es der__ Ge - bie - te - rin,
Nach - barn a - ber, Nach - barn nicht,
find my true__ be - lov - ed's ear,
for no o - ther ear__ but hers!

send__ es der__ Ge - bie - te - rin!
Nach - barn a - ber,__ Nach - barn nicht!
find__ my true__ be - lov - ed's ear!
for__ no o - ther__ ear but hers!

Fine

Blow The Wind Southerly starts on B, the third note of the scale of G major.

I   II   III   IV   V   VI   VII   I'

Blow The Wind Southerly

Northumbrian Spiritual

Andante
mf

Blow the wind sou - ther- ly, sou -ther- ly, sou -ther- ly, Blow the wind south o'er the bon - ny blue sea.

Blow the wind sou - ther- ly, sou - ther- ly, sou -ther- ly, Blow bon-ny bree - zes my lov - er to me. They

told me last night there were ships in the off - ing, And I hur - ried down to the deep rol - ling sea, but my

eye could not see it wher - ev - er might be it, The bark that is bear - ing my lov - er to me.

8

Ornaments in Music

Notes are often decorated with *ornaments*. Three types are used in this book.

The Appoggiatura. A small-sized note, written before the principal note. It takes half the time of the principal note, unless the principal note is dotted, in which case it takes two-thirds of the time (see also page 10).

Sandmännchen (The Little Sandman) is a mythical German fairy said to be able to put children gently to sleep by scattering magic sand in their eyes. Notice that it starts on the fifth note (D) of the scale, and that this is the D *below* the first keynote, G. Songs which begin in this way can be preceded by the arpeggio, then the notes I, III, V and lower V like this:

Sandmännchen
(The Sandman)

Johannes Brahms
Words traditional
Translated by E.D. Turnbull

(for v.2, D.C. al Fine)   **Fine**

More Ornaments

The Acciaccatura. A small-sized note, written before the principal note. It is played quickly, taking its time from the principal note. It has a stroke through the top of the stem.

The Turn. A turn consists of the note *above* the principal note, the principal note, the note *below* the principal note and the principal note again. The four notes *together* must be equal in time to the principal note.

Die Zufriedenheit contains turns and an appoggiatura. It is in 6/8 time. As the song is about contentment, it needs to be presented in an appropriate way. Sing it with gentleness, and with a facial expression that suggests pleasure, but without exaggeration.

Die Zufriedenheit
(Contentment)

W.A. Mozart, K.473
Words by C.F. Weisse
Translated by E.D. Turnbull

Part 3

Songs in D, A, E and B Majors

D major has two sharps – F♯ and C♯.

Sacramento

Traditional Sea Shanty

Allegro ma non troppo

f 1. A - round Cape Horn   we're bound to go,   } Sac - ra - men - to, Sac - ra - men - to,   { A -
mp 2. A - round Cape Horn in the month of May,   }   { A -
f 3. To the Sa - cra - men - to we're bound a - way   }   { To the

- round Cape Horn through the sleet and snow   } To the banks o' Sac - ra - men - to,
- round Cape Horn is a very long way   }
Sac - ra - men - to's a long, long way   }

Blow, blow,____ blow, for Cal - i - forn - ia, O! There's

plen - ty of gold so I've been told on the banks o' Sac - ra - men - to.

A major has three sharps – F♯, C♯ and G♯.

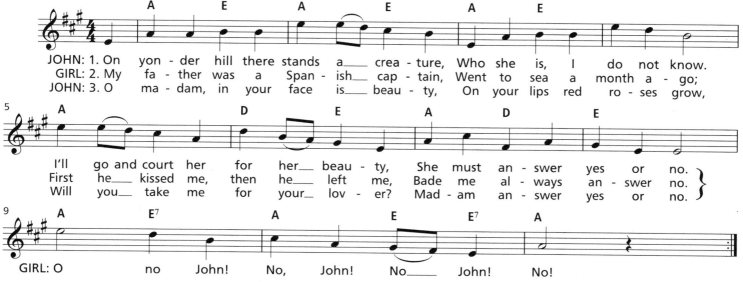

In the following piece, try to get a contrast between the words sung by John, and those sung by the Girl.

O No, John!

English Traditional

Allegro moderato

JOHN: 1. On yon - der hill there stands a____ crea - ture, Who she is, I do not know.
GIRL: 2. My fa - ther was a Span - ish____ cap - tain, Went to sea a month a - go;
JOHN: 3. O ma - dam, in your face is____ beau - ty, On your lips red ro - ses grow,

I'll go and court her for her____ beau - ty, She must an - swer yes or no.
First he____ kissed me, then he____ left me, Bade me al - ways an - swer no.
Will you____ take me for your____ lov - er? Mad - am an - swer yes or no.

GIRL: O no John! No, John! No____ John! No!

Man Is For The Woman Made has two minim beats to the bar. Sing it rhythmically, and with spirit. The words must be very clear.

Man Is For The Woman Made
Roundelay

Henry Purcell
Words by John Motteaux
Arranged by David Turnbull

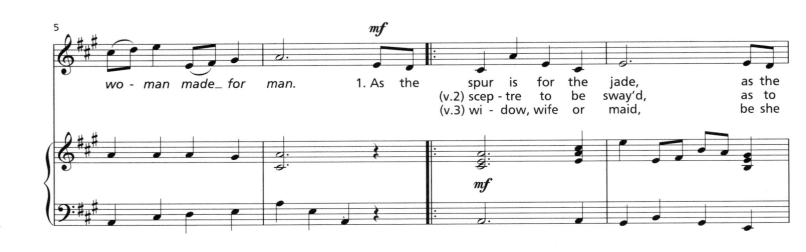

E major has four sharps – F♯, C♯, G♯ and D♯. *Rio Grande* starts on the fifth note of E major, B.

I   II   III   IV   V   VI   VII   I'

Rio Grande

Traditional British Sea Shanty

Allegro

1. Oh, where are you go-ing to,   my pret-ty maid?
2. Oh, what is your for - tune,   my pret-ty maid?
3. Oh, then I can't mar-ry you,   my pret-ty maid.

Oh_____ to Ri - o_____

"I'm
"My
"Oh,

go - ing a milk - ing sir,"__ she said.
face is my for - tune, sir,"__ she said.
no - bo - dy ask'd__ you sir,"__ she said.

But we're bound for the Ri - o Grande. Then a

way,   love__ a - way,_____   Way_____ for Ri - o,_____ So

fare__ ye well__ my bon - ny young lass, for we're bound for the Ri - o Grande.__

B major has five sharps – F♯, C♯, G♯, D♯ and A♯. This key is used infrequently.

I   II   III   IV   V   VI   VII   I'

Annie Laurie

Scottish Traditional

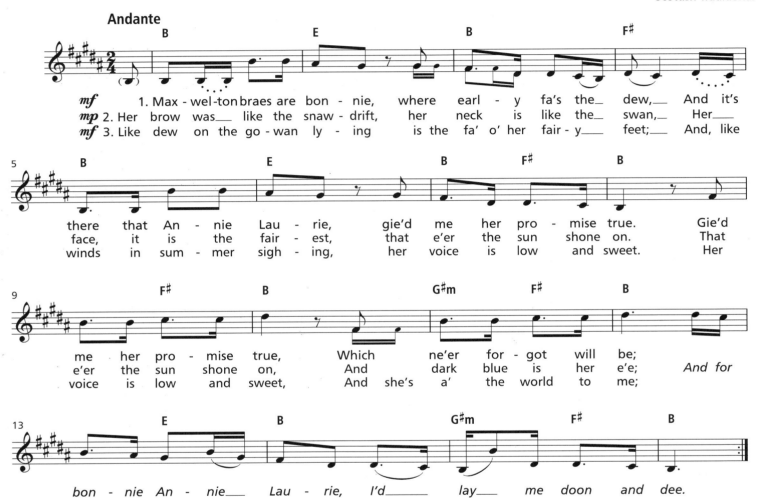

Andante

mf 1. Max - wel -ton braes are bon - nie, where earl - y fa's the dew, And it's

mp 2. Her brow was like the snaw - drift, her neck is like the swan, Her

mf 3. Like dew on the go - wan ly - ing is the fa' o' her fair - y feet; And, like

there that An - nie Lau - rie, gie'd me her pro - mise true. Gie'd

face, it is the fair - est, that e'er the sun shone on. That

winds in sum - mer sigh - ing, her voice is low and sweet. Her

me her pro - mise true, Which ne'er for - got will be;

e'er the sun shone on, And dark blue is her e'e;

voice is low and sweet, And she's a' the world to me; *And for*

bon - nie An - nie Lau - rie, I'd lay me doon and dee.

Part 4

Songs in Major Keys Using Flats

F major has one flat – B♭.

I   II   III   IV   V   VI   VII   I'

O Mistress Mine
(from Twelfth Night)

Charles Villiers Stanford
Words by William Shakespeare

Allegretto con moto

O mis-tress mine! Where are you roam - ing? O stay and hear; your true love's com - ing that can sing___ both high___ and low. Trip no fur - ther, pret-ty

sweet - ing; journ - eys end in lo - vers meet - ing,

Ev - 'ry wise___ man's son doth___ know

What is love? 'Tis not here - -af - ter; pre - sent mirth___ hath pre - sent laugh - ter; What's to

come___ is still___ un - sure; In de-

-lay there lies no plen - ty; then come kiss me,

sweet and twen - ty, youth's a stuff will not en -

- dure.___

Blow, Blow, Thou Winter Wind!

Thomas Arne
Words by William Shakespeare

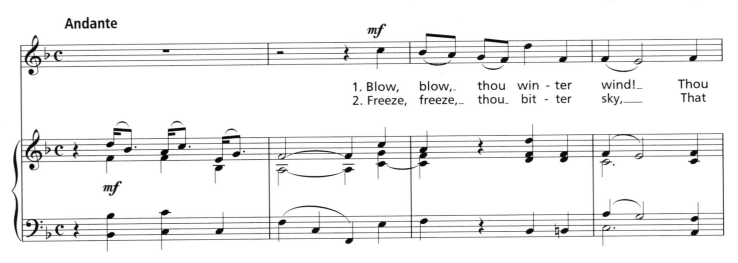

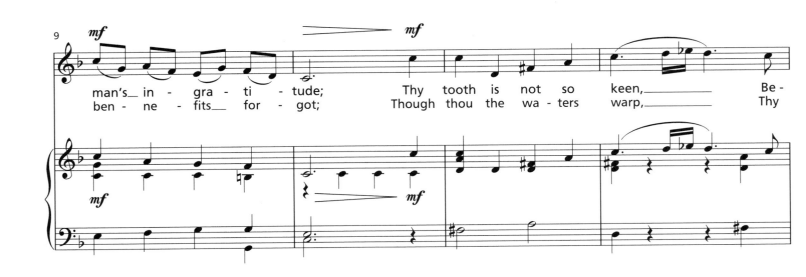

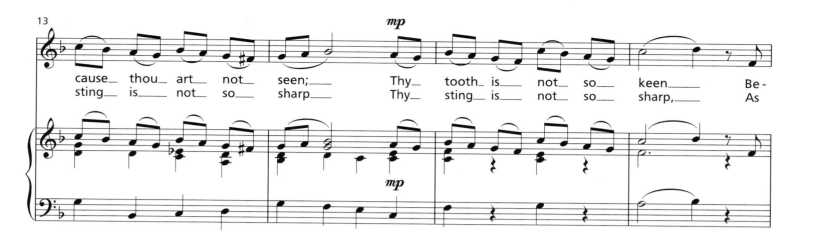

cause_ thou_ art_ not_ seen;_ Thy_ tooth_ is_ not_ so_ keen_____ Be -
sting_ is_ not_ so_ sharp_____ Thy_ sting_ is_ not_ so_ sharp,_____ As

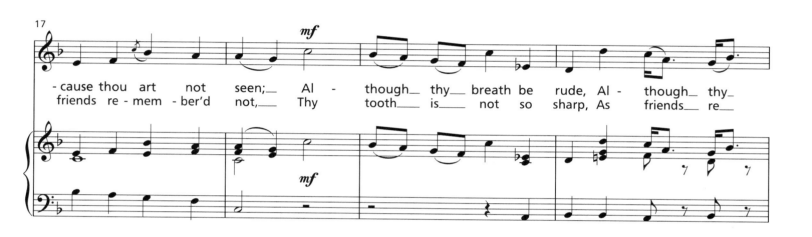

- cause thou art not seen;_ Al - though_ thy_ breath be rude, Al - though_ thy_
friends re - mem - ber'd not,_ Thy tooth_ is_ not so sharp, As friends_ re_

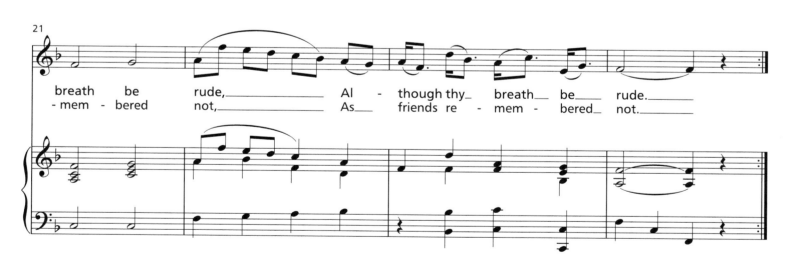

breath be rude,_____ Al - though thy_ breath_ be_ rude._____
- mem - bered not,_____ As_ friends re - mem - bered_ not._____

B♭ **major** has two flats – B♭ and E♭.

I   II   III   IV   V   VI   VII   I'

The next two songs, *Salley In Our Alley* and *Consider Yourself* are in B♭ major. *Consider Yourself* is a song from the show *Oliver* and it can be presented more dramatically than most of the songs in this book (see the comments on page 5).

Salley In Our Alley

English, possibly by Henry Carey
Arranged by G. Macfarren

1. Of all the girls___ that are so smart___ there's
(v.2) days___ with-in the week,___ I

none like pret-ty Sal-ley! She is the dar-ling of my heart,___ and lives in our___
dear-ly love but one day, and that's the day___ that comes be-twixt___ a Sa-tur-day___ and

al-ley; there is no la-dy in the land that's half so sweet___ as Sal-ley; she is the
Mon-day; oh then I'm dress'd, all in my best, to walk a-broad___ with Sal-ley; she is the

dar-ling of my heart,___ and lives in our_____ al-ley. 2. Of all the
dar-ling of my heart,___ and lives in our_____ al-ley.

Consider Yourself
(from Oliver)

Words and Music by Lionel Bart

Since First I Saw Your Face

Thomas Ford
Arranged by G. Macfarren

Andante e legato

One Hand, One Heart
(from West Side Story)

Music by Leonard Bernstein
Words by Stephen Sondheim

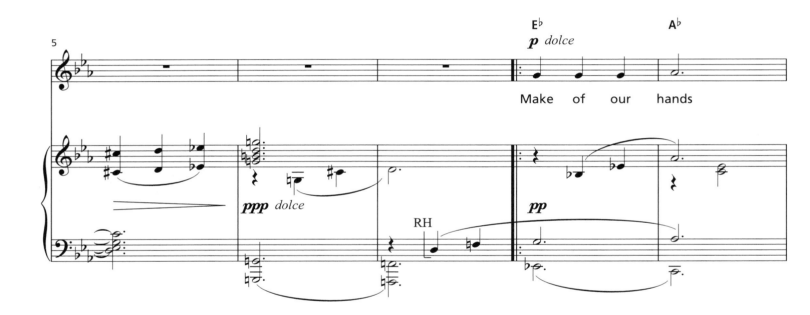

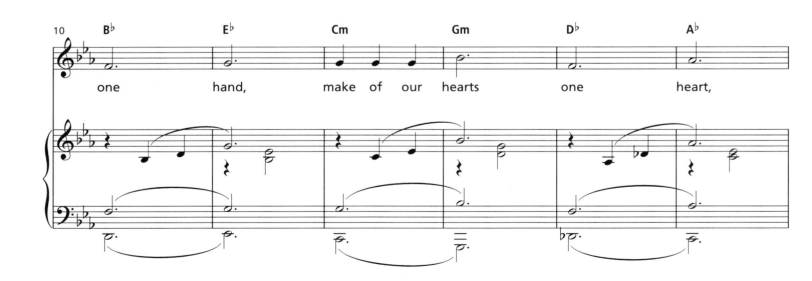

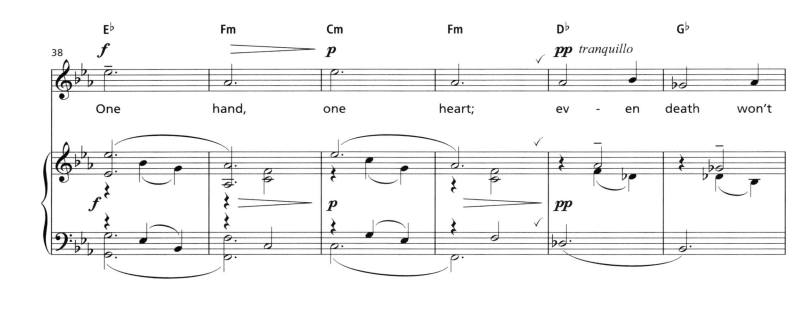

One hand, one heart; ev - en death won't

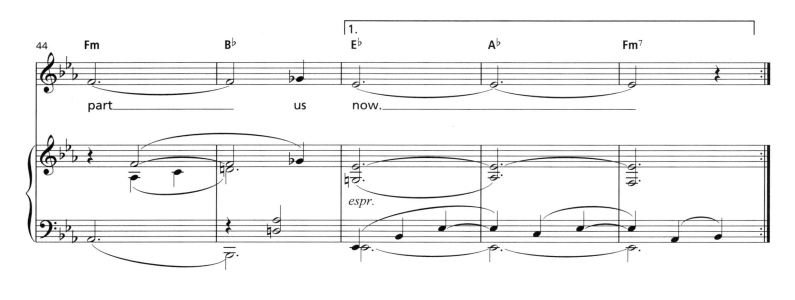

part_____ us now._____

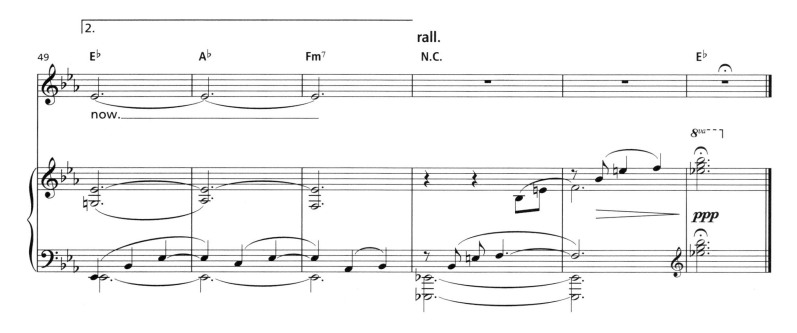

now._____

A♭ major has four flats – B♭, E♭, A♭ and D♭.

I   II   III   IV   V   VI   VII   I'

Abendlied
(Evening Song)

Franz Schubert, D.499
Words by M. Claudius
Translated by E.D. Turnbull

1. Der Mond ist auf - ge - gan - en; die gold - nen Stern - lein
2. Wie ist die Welt so stil - le, und in der Dämm - rung
1. The sil - ver moon has ris - en, the gold - en star - lets
2. By sil - ence now the world's en - dowed, the fad - ing twi - light

pran - gen am Him - mel hell__ und klar; der Wald steht schwarz und
Hül - le so trau - lich und__ so hold! Als ei - ne stil - le
glis - ten, in skies__ so clear__ and bright. The wood stands mute and
casts its shroud, so com - fort - ing,__ and fair! As if with - in some

schwei - get und aus den Wie - sen stei - get der wei - sse Ne - bel
Kam - mer, wo ihr des Ta - ges Jam - mer ver - schla - fen und__ ver -
dark - ling, and from the mea - dows ris - ing come mists__ so fine__ and
cham - ber, the noise and dai - ly clam - our gives way__ to sleep and ob -

wun - der - bar!
- ges - sen sollt!
won - drous - ly white!
- liv - ion so rare!

Verses 3 and 4:

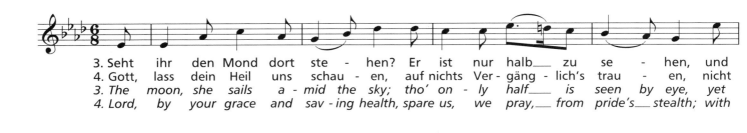

3. Seht ihr den Mond dort ste - hen? Er ist nur halb__ zu se - hen, und
4. Gott, lass dein Heil uns schau - en, auf nichts Ver - gäng - lich's trau - en, nicht
3. *The moon, she sails a - mid the sky; tho' on - ly half__ is seen by eye, yet*
4. *Lord, by your grace and sav - ing health, spare us, we pray,__ from pride's__ stealth; with*

ist__ doch rund__ und schön! So sind wohl man - che Sa - chen, die
Ei - tel - keit__ uns freun! Lass uns ein - fäl - tig wer - den, und
round__ and fair__ is she! So too are ma - ny things on earth we
love__ our hearts__ ex - pand! May we em - brace sim - pli - ci - ty, on

wir ge - trost__ be - la - chen, weil un - sre Au - gen sie__ nicht sehn.
vor dir hier__ auf Er - den wie Kin - der fromm__ und fröh - lich sein!
scorn - ful - ly__ dis - miss__ with mirth, Be - cause__ our sen - ses can - not see.
earth with deep__ fe - li - ci - ty; like child - ren joy - ous be - fore Thee to stand!

D♭ major. The key of D♭ major has not been explained in *Singing Time!* Grades 1-3, so look carefully at its key signature.

D♭ major has five flats – B♭, E♭, A♭, D♭ and G♭.

I   II   III   IV   V   VI   VII   I'

The Harp That Once Through Tara's Halls

Irish Traditional
Words by Moore

Moderato

1. The harp that once through Ta - ra's halls its soul of mu - sic shed, Now
2. No more to chiefs and la - dies bright the harp of Ta - ra swells; The

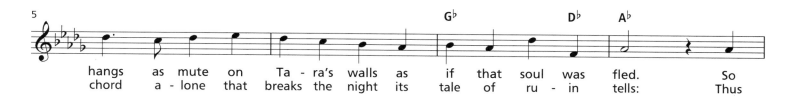

hangs as mute on Ta - ra's walls as if that soul was fled. So
chord a - lone that breaks the night its tale of ru - in tells: Thus

sleeps the pride of___ for - mer days, so glo - ry's thrill is o'er; And
free - dom now so___ sel - dom wakes; the on - ly throb she gives Is

hearts that once beat high for praise now feel that pulse no more.
when some heart in - dig - nant breaks to show that still she lives.

Part 5

Beyond Major Keys

The next three songs are all in minor keys. *Joshua Fit De Battle Of Jericho* is in **D minor**, *Die Waise* in **G minor**, and *O Cessate Di Piagarmi* in **F minor**.
Be particularly careful of the tuning of the sharpened leading note (note VII) of each scale when it appears. (For more information, see *Theory Time* Grade 3, pp. 15-20.)

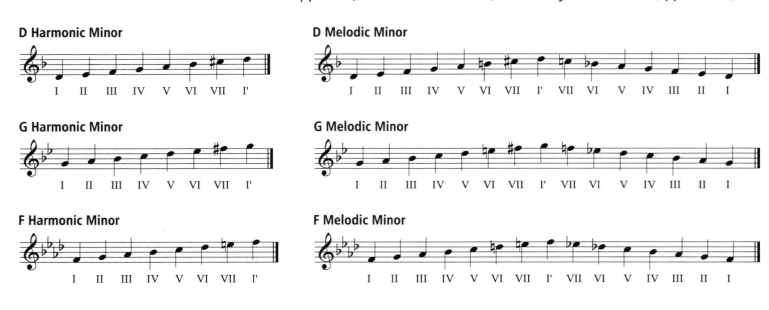

This spiritual needs to be sung with really firm rhythm.

Joshua Fit De Battle Of Jericho

Afro-American Spiritual

Chorus: Josh - ua fit de bat - tle of Je - ri - cho,_ Je - ri - cho,_ Je - ri - cho,_

Josh - ua fit de bat - tle of Je - ri - cho__ and the walls come tum - bl - in' down.

1. You can talk a - bout your King of Gi - de - on, You can talk a - bout your man of
2. So up to the walls of Je - ri - cho, He march'd_ with sword in

D.C. al Fine

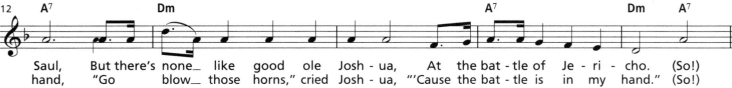

Saul, But there's none_ like good ole Josh - ua, At the bat - tle of Je - ri - cho. (So!)
hand, "Go blow_ those horns," cried Josh - ua, "'Cause the bat - tle is in my hand." (So!)

Die Waise
(The Orphan)

Robert Schumann
Words by von Hallersleben
Translated by E.D. Turnbull

Langsam

1. Der Früh - ling keh - ret wie - der, und al - les freu - et sich, ich
2. Was soll mir ar - men Kin - de des Früh - lings Pracht und Glanz? Denn
1. *The Spring re - turns with glad - ness, and joy is in the air. I*
2. *Poor child - ren see its splen - dours, but can - not feel its joy. For*

bli - cke trau - rig nie - der, er kam ja nicht für mich. 3. Ach!
wenn ich Blu - men win - de, ist es zum To - ten - kranz. 4. O
look a - round with sad - ness; for Spring to me brings care. 3. Oh!
as I weave the flow - ers, death's wreath's my on - ly toy. 4. O

kei - ne Hand ge - lei - tet mich heim ins Va - ter - haus, und
Him - mel, gib mir wie - der, was dei - ne Lie - be gab und blick
No hand guides me gent - ly to - ward my fa - ther's home, no
hea - ven, grant me once more your gift of love to me. When

kei - ne Mut - ter brei - tet die Ar - me nach mir aus.
ich zur Er - de nie - der, so seh ich nur ihr Grab.
moth - er's arms so soft - ly show me I'm not a - lone.
I my glance do low - er, a tomb is all I see.

Schluß

O Cessate Di Piagarmi is a famous old Italian song. It is best sung in Italian for its full effect. Ask for some help from an Italian speaker. The letter 'c', for example, if followed by an 'e' or an 'i' is *soft*, rather like the 'ch' in 'church'.

O Cessate Di Piagarmi

Alessandro Scarlatti, Arranged by A. Parisotti
Text: N. Minato, Translated by David Turnbull

Andante con moto

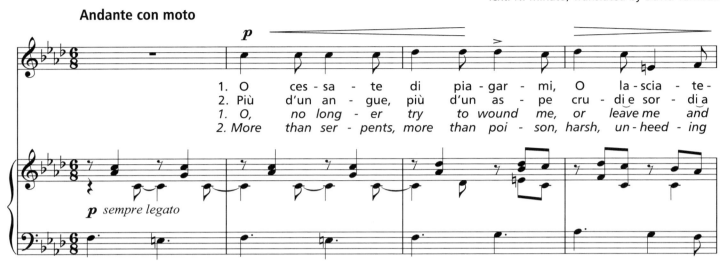

più del mar - mi Fred - de e sor - de a' miei mar - tir, Fred - de e sor___ de a'
ri - sa - nar - mi, E go - de - te al mio lan - guir, E go - de - te al
so freeze me,___ Or re - ject me so ut - ter - ly, Or re - ject me so
grief and tor - ment, But you smile at my mi - se - ry, But you smile at my

miei mar - tir. }
mio lan - guir. }
ut - ter - ly. }
mi - se - ry. }
O ces - sa - te di pia - gar - mi, O la - scia - te -
O, no lon - ger try to wound me, Or leave me and

- mi mo - rir, O la - scia - te - mi mo - rir.
let me die, Or leave me and let me die.

The next two songs are written in *modes*, rather than major or minor scales. There are a number of different modes. All you need to know now is in the modes featured in the next two songs, the seventh note of the mode is a tone below the top tonic. In major, harmonic minor and *ascending* melodic minor scales, there is a semitone between the two highest notes. Many folk songs are in modes.

All The Pretty Little Horses

American Traditional Lullaby

Slowly and gently

1. Hush - a - bye, don't you cry, Go to sleep - y lit - tle ba - by
2. When you wake you shall have All the pret - ty lit - tle

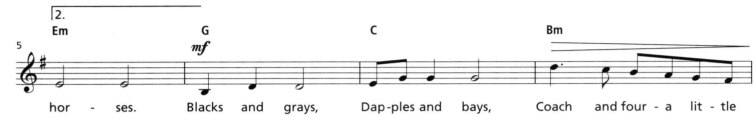

hor - ses. Blacks and grays, Dap-ples and bays, Coach and four - a lit - tle

hor - ses. Hush - a - bye, don't you cry, Go to sleep-y lit -tle ba - by.

She's Like The Swallow

Newfoundland Traditional

Andante doloroso

1. She's like the swal - low that flies so high; She's like the ri - ver that
2. She climbed on yon - der hill a - bove To give a rose un -
3. And as they sat on yon - der hill His heart grew hard, so

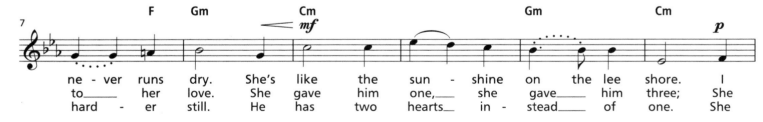

ne - ver runs dry. She's like the sun - shine on the lee shore. I
to her love. She gave him one, she gave him three; She
hard - er still. He has two hearts in - stead of one. She

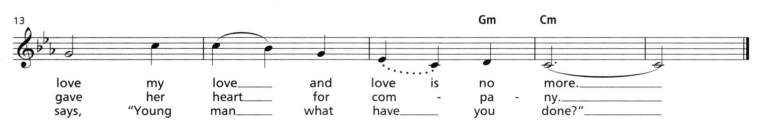

love my love and love is no more.
gave her heart for com - pa - ny.
says, "Young man what have you done?"

4. 'How foolish, foolish you must be
   To think I love no-one but thee.
   The world's not made for one alone,
   I take delight in everyone.'

5. She took her roses and made a bed,
   A stony pillow for her head.
   She lay her down, no more did say,
   But let her roses fall away.

Part 6

Singing At Sight

Singing at sight needs frequent practice.

In examinations, you are allowed half a minute to prepare the test. When practising, take as much time as is necessary – you will get faster with experience.

In examinations, you are allowed to sing the notes to the printed words, *or* to any vowel, *or* to sol-fa names. When practising, it is best to sing the words, as they help you to understand the mood of the song.

Look at piece **1** below.
- · Work out the rhythmic pattern. Clap the rhythm of the introduction, then the words.
- · Decide what key the piece is in and on which note of the scale it starts. See if your starting note is played by the piano in the introduction. Here, the key is E♭ major, and your starting note, B♭, is sounded by the piano in bar 1.
- · The melody will be a mixture of stepwise movement and jumps. Work out the intervals of any jumps before you start.
- · Look at the dynamics and any expression marks and be sure to include them.
- · Sing the song slowly at first. When confident, sing it at its suggested tempo.

Now sing **1** below. Use the same method for the other pieces.

1

Words by Edward Lear

Words by Edward Lear

Brightly

Said the Duck to the Kan - ga - roo, "Good

gra - cious! How you hop! O - ver the hills and the wa - ter too, as

senza rit.

if you would ne - ver stop, stop, stop, as if you would ne - ver stop!"

Words by William Shakespeare
(from Cymbeline)

Lento e mesto

Fear no more the heat of the sun,

nor the fur - ious win - ter ra - ges, thou thy world - ly task__ hast done,

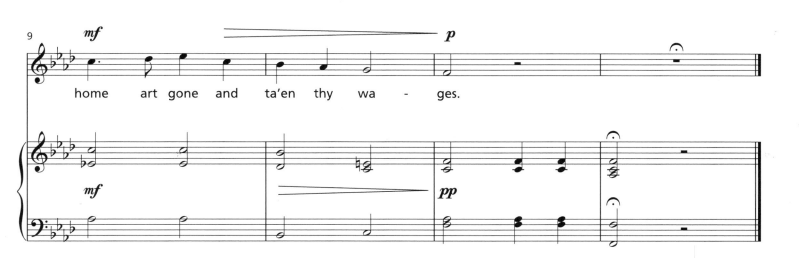

home art gone and ta'en thy wa - ges.

Collected and Arranged by Cecil J. Sharp

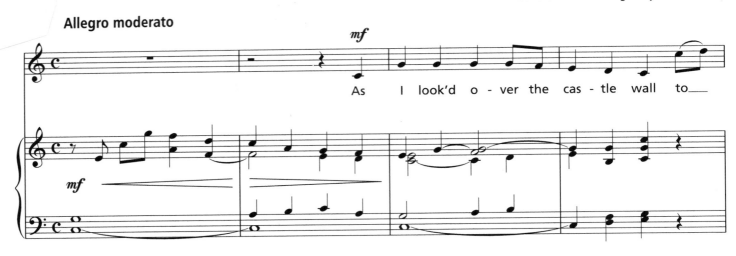

5

Words by Gerard Manley Hopkins

I have de-sired to go where springs not fail, to fields where flies no sharp and sid-ed hail and a few li-lies blow.

6

Words by Thomas Hood

Take her up ten-der-ly, lift her with care, fash-ion'd so slen-der-ly, young and so fair! Young and so fair!

English Traditional
Arranged by G. Macfarren

Allegro non troppo

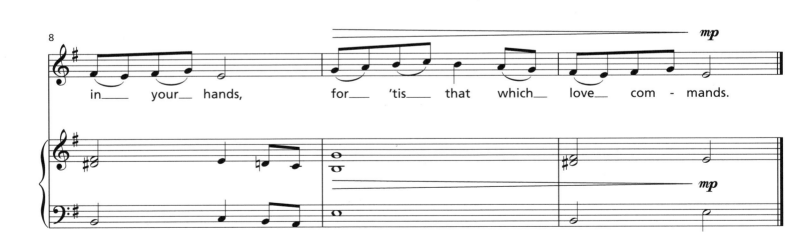

German Traditional
Music by Weber

Words by William Blake

Lento e mesto

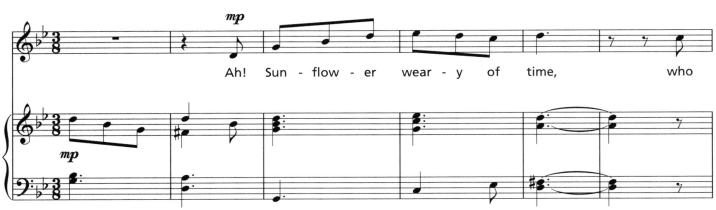

Ah! Sun - flow - er wear - y of time, who

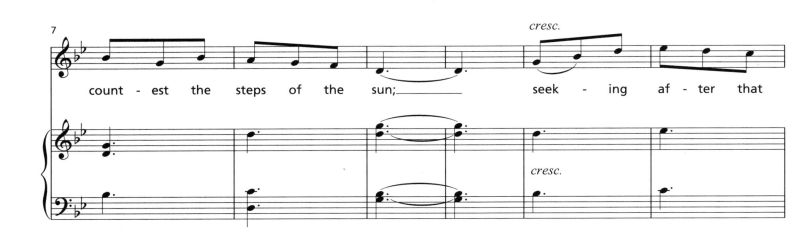

count - est the steps of the sun; _____ seek - ing af - ter that

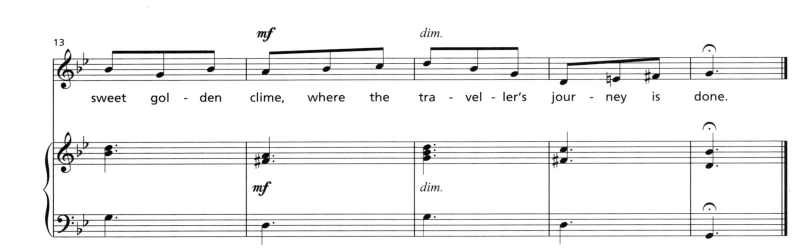

sweet gol - den clime, where the tra - vel - ler's jour - ney is done.

English Ballad

Moderato e grazioso

Now when Lord__ Bar - nard__ heard__ the__ page, a

loud laugh__ laugh - ed____ he, and said,__ I____ know a____

hun - dred____ maids, each____ one as fair as she.

Remember that any song in this book that is unknown to you may be used as extra sight-singing practice.

Some Italian and German Terms used in this book
(Italian unless otherwise indicated)

Allegretto	Fairly fast, but less fast than *allegro*
Allegretto e molto ritmico	(as *Allegretto*) and very rhythmic
Allegro	Fairly fast
Allegro ma non troppo	Fairly fast, but not too much so
Allegro moderato	Moderately fast
Allegro vivace	Fast and lively
Andante	Walking pace
Andante con moto	Walking pace, but with movement
Andante doloroso	Walking pace, but sadly
Andante e legato	Walking pace, and smoothly
Con moto	With movement
Crescendo (cresc.)	Gradually getting louder
Da Capo (D.C.)	From the beginning
Da Capo (D.C.) al Fine	From the beginning to the end
Dal Segno (D.S.) or D.𝄋	Go back to the sign 𝄋
Decrescendo	Gradually getting quieter
Diminuendo (dim.)	Gradually getting quieter
Etwas geschwind (Ger.)	Rather fast
Langsam (Ger.)	Slow
Legato	Smoothly
Lento	Slowly
Lento e mesto	Slowly and sadly
Mesto	Sadly
Moderato	At a moderate speed, neither fast nor slow
Moderato e grazioso	*Moderato* (see above) and gracefully
Rallentando	Getting slower gradually
Ritenuto (rit.)	Slow the tempo
Ruhig (Ger.)	Peaceful
Schluss (or Schluß) (Ger.)	End
Sempre legato	Always smooth
Senza ritenuto	Without slowing down

Index of songs

09/07 (63515)